UNFORGETTABLE...

PIANO SOLOS

The Magic of the Musicals

Wise Publications
London / New York / Paris / Sydney / Copenhagen / Madrid

Exclusive Distributors:
Music Sales Limited
8/9 Frith Street,
London W1V 5TZ, England.
Music Sales Pty Limited
120 Rothschild Avenue,
Rosebery, NSW 2018,
Australia.

Order No. AM951390
ISBN 0-7119-7107-2
This book © Copyright 1998 by Wise Publications

Music compiled by Peter Evans
Book design by Pearce Marchbank, Studio Twenty, London
Computer layout by Ben May

Printed in the United Kingdom by
Redwood Books Limited, Trowbridge, Wiltshire.

Your Guarantee of Quality
As publishers, we strive to produce every book to the highest
commercial standards. This book has been carefully designed to
minimise awkward page turns and to make playing from it a real
pleasure. Particular care has been given to specifying acid-free,
neutral-sized paper made from pulps which have not been
elemental chlorine bleached. This pulp is from farmed sustainable
forests and was produced with special regard for the environment.
Throughout, the printing and binding have been planned to ensure a
sturdy, attractive publication which should give years of enjoyment.
If your copy fails to meet our high standards, please inform us
and we will gladly replace it.

Music Sales' complete catalogue describes thousands of titles
and is available in full colour sections by subject, direct from
Music Sales Limited. Please state your areas of interest and
send a cheque/postal order for £1.50 for postage to:
Music Sales Limited, Newmarket Road,
Bury St. Edmunds, Suffolk IP33 3YB.

Visit the Internet Music Shop at
http://www.musicsales.co.uk

All I Ask Of You

Music by Andrew Lloyd Webber
Lyrics by Charles Hart. Additional Lyrics by Richard Stilgoe

Anthem

Words & Music by Benny Andersson, Tim Rice & Bjorn Ulvaeus

Another Suitcase In Another Hall

Music by Andrew Lloyd Webber
Lyrics by Tim Rice

As If We Never Said Goodbye

Music by Andrew Lloyd Webber
Lyrics by Don Black & Christopher Hampton
with contributions by Amy Powers

D.C. al Coda

15

Big Spender

Words by Dorothy Fields
Music by Cy Coleman

Aggressively, with swing

Close Every Door

Music by Sir Andrew Lloyd Webber
Lyrics by Tim Rice

Moderately, with expression

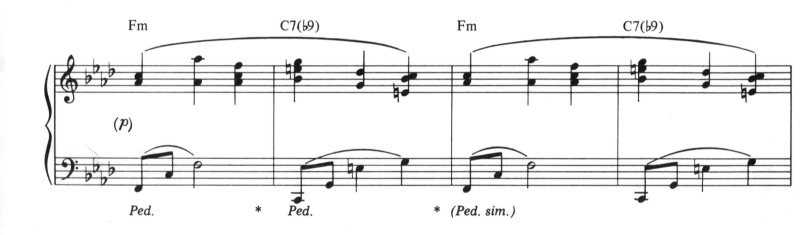

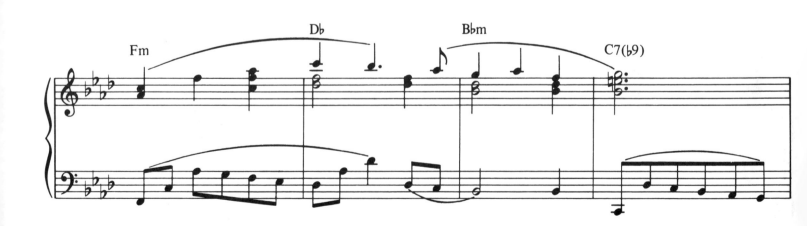

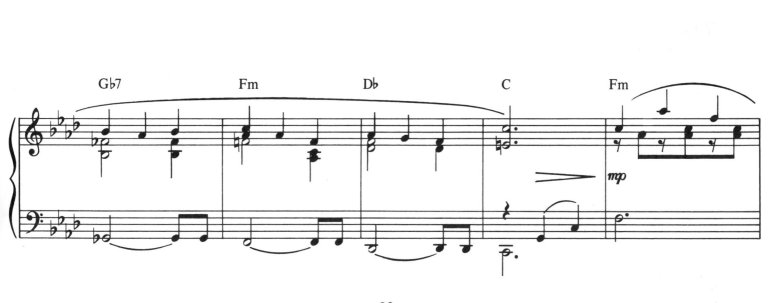

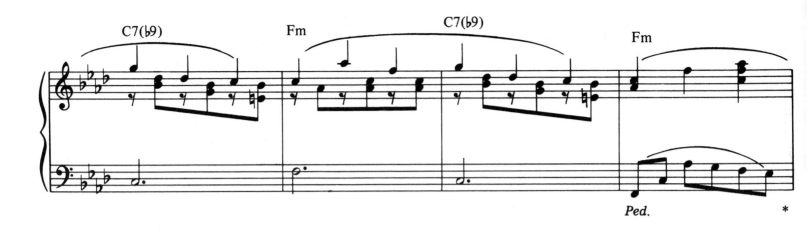

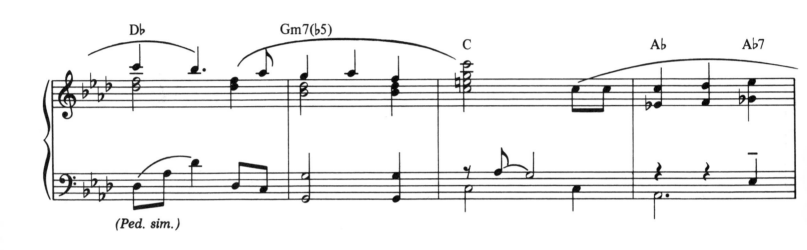

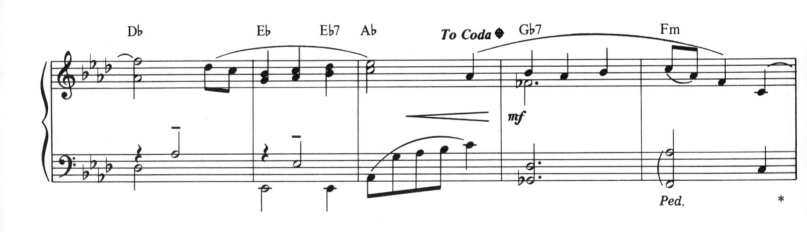

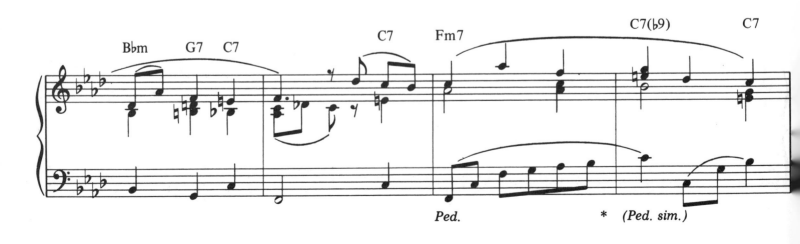

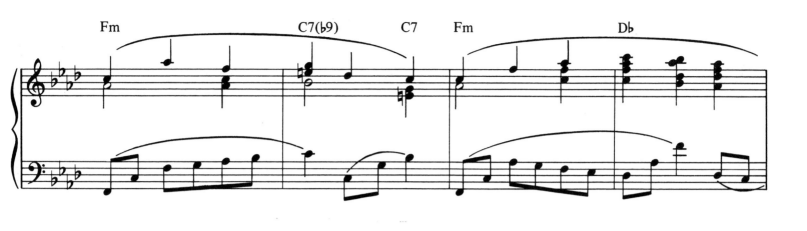

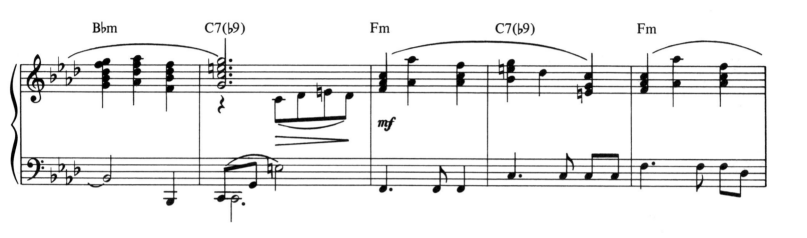

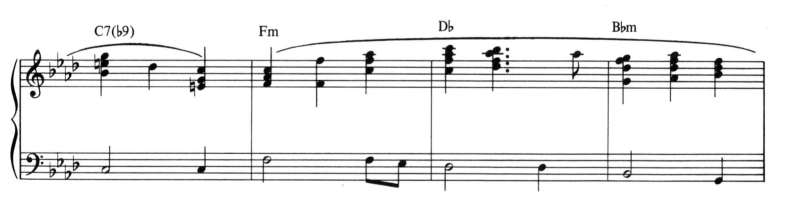

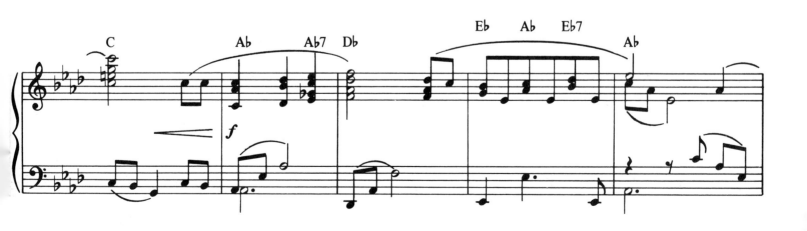

25

I'd Give My Life For You

Music by Claude-Michel Schönberg. Lyrics by Richard Maltby Jr. & Alain Boublil
Adapted from the original French Lyrics by Alain Boublil

31

I Dreamed A Dream

Music by Claude-Michel Schönberg. Lyric by Herbert Kretzmer
Original Text by Alain Boublil & Jean-Marc Natel

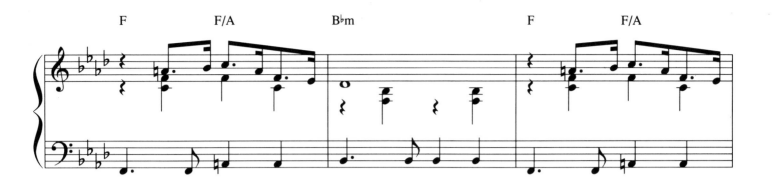

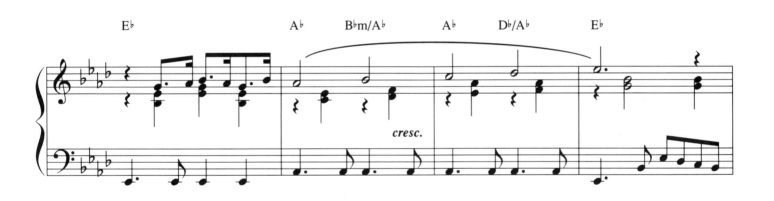

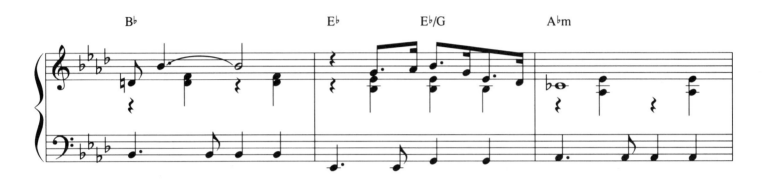

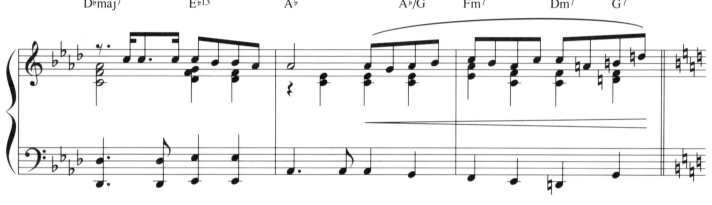

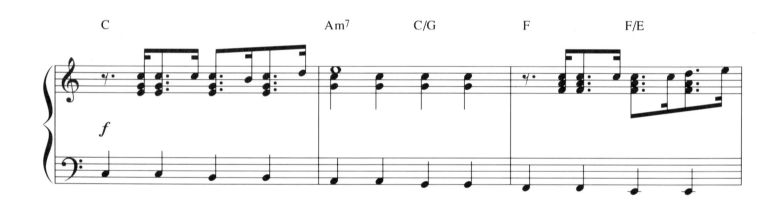

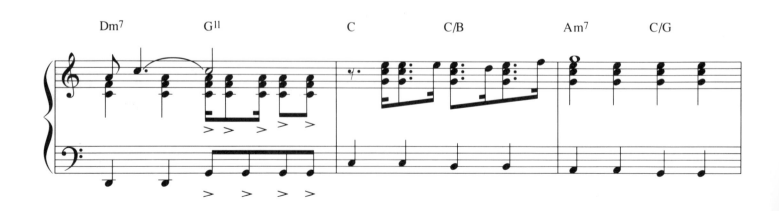

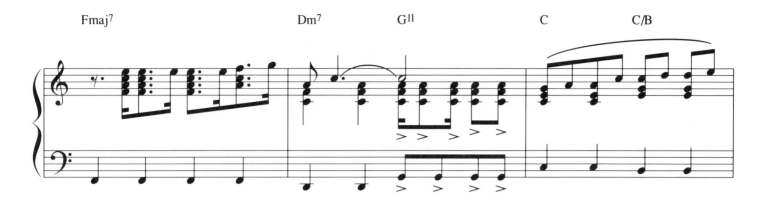

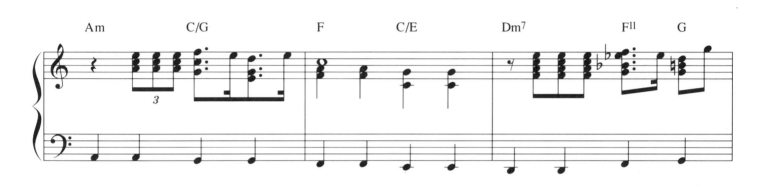

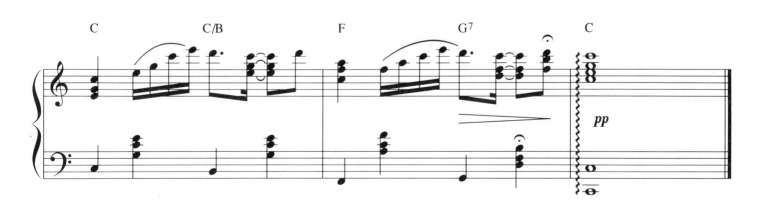

Luck Be A Lady

Words & Music by Frank Loesser

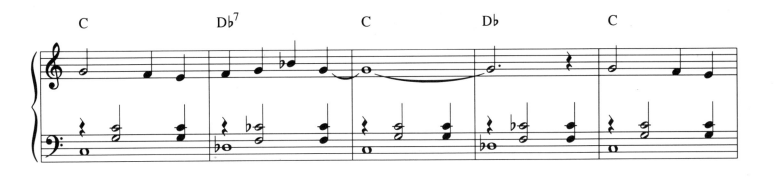

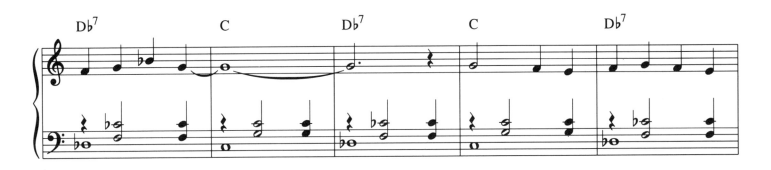

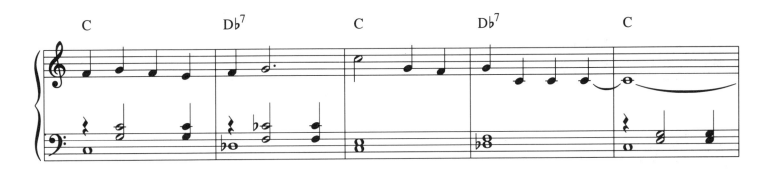

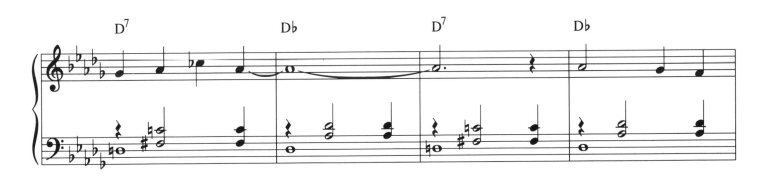

It Ain't Necessarily So

Words & Music by George Gershwin, DuBose & Dorothy Heyward & Ira Gershwin

Moderately

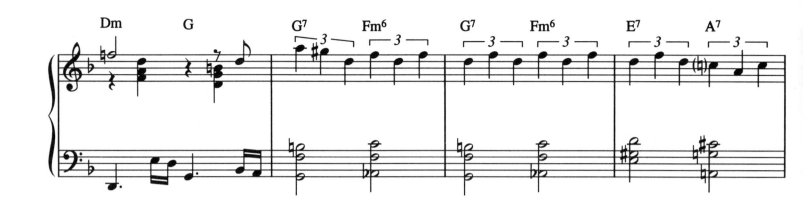

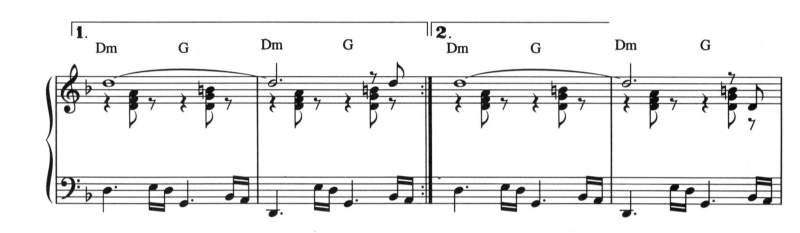

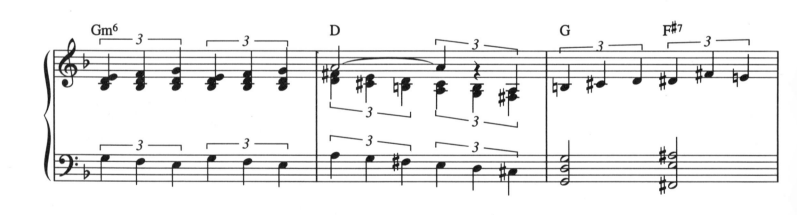

Now That I've Seen Her

Music by Claude-Michel Schönberg
Lyrics by Richard Maltby Jr. & Alain Boublil

poco cresc.

44

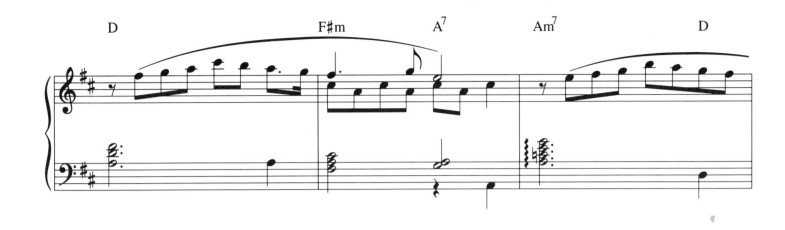

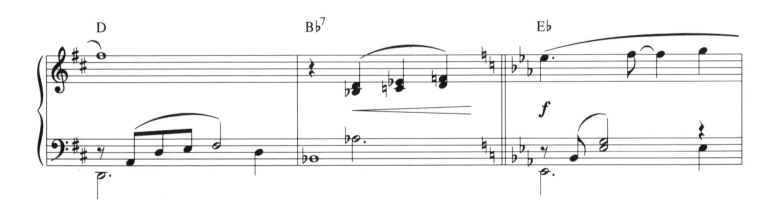

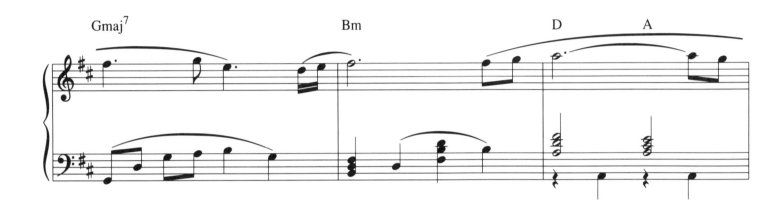

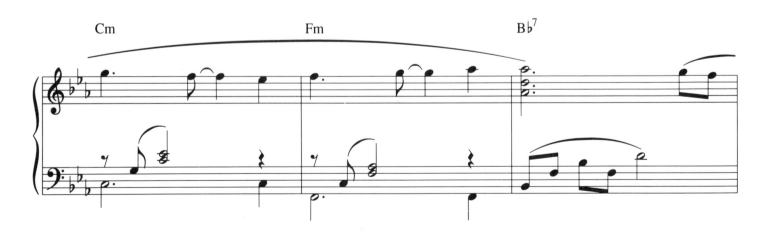

46

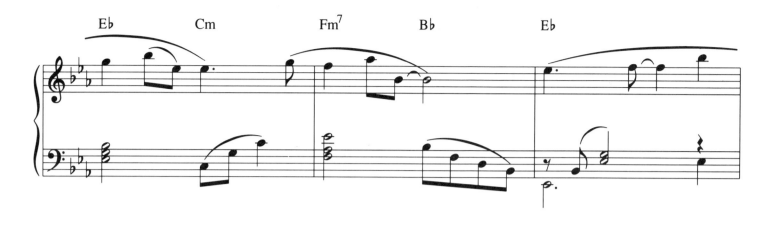

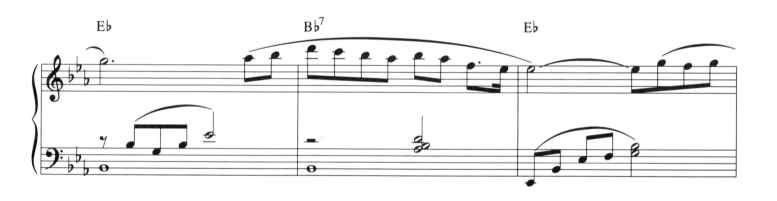

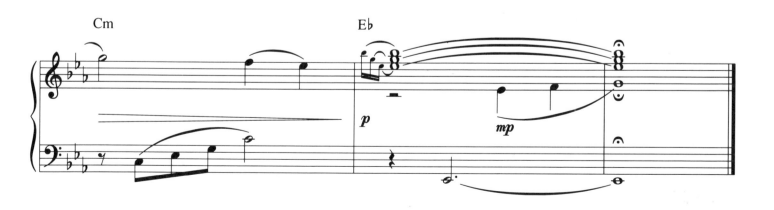

Pick A Pocket Or Two

Words & Music by Lionel Bart

On My Own

Music by Claude-Michel Schönberg. Lyric by Herbert Kretzmer
Original Text by Alain Boublil & Jean-Marc Natel

Send In The Clowns

Words & Music by Stephen Sondheim

Sun And Moon

Music by Claude-Michel Schönberg. Lyrics by Richard Maltby Jr. & Alain Boublil
Adapted from original French Lyrics by Alain Boublil

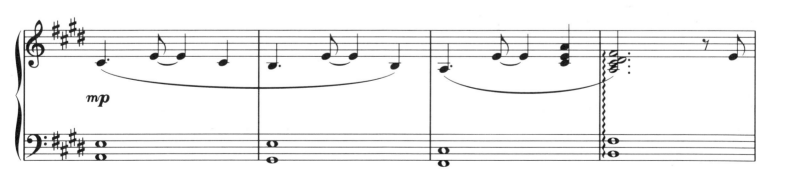

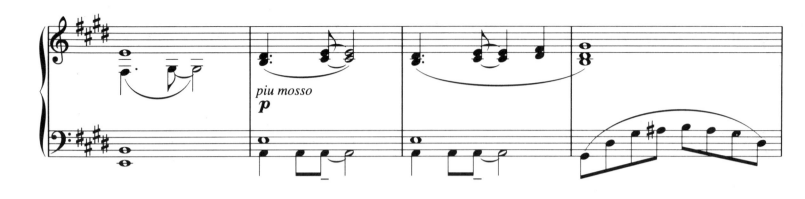

Take That Look Off Your Face

Music by Andrew Lloyd Webber
Lyrics by Don Black

Tell Me On A Sunday

Music by Andrew Lloyd Webber
Lyrics by Don Black

The Music Of The Night

Music by Andrew Lloyd Webber
Lyrics by Charles Hart. Additional lyrics by Richard Stilgoe

The Last Night Of The World

Music by Claude-Michel Schönberg. Lyrics by Richard Maltby Jr. & Alain Boublil
Adapted from the original French Lyrics by Alain Boublil

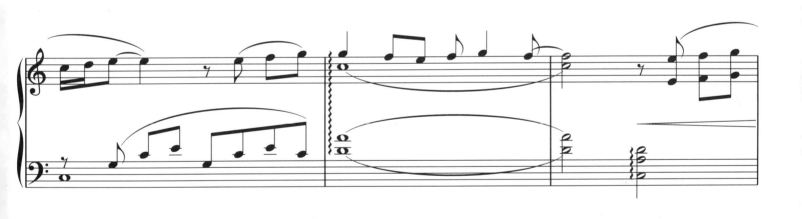

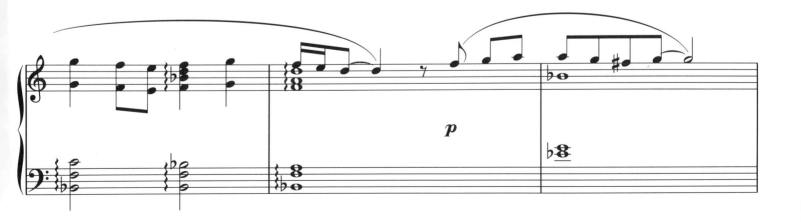

Tomorrow

Music by Charles Strouse
Words by Martin Charnin

Tonight

Music by Leonard Bernstein
Lyrics by Stephen Sondheim

Moderate Beguine Tempo